TODAY'S HITS

WISE PUBLICATIONS

PART OF THE MUSIC SALES GROUP

LONDON / NEW YORK / PARIS / SYDNEY / COPENHAGEN / BERLIN / MADRID / HONG KONG / TOKYO

PUBLISHED BY
WISE PUBLICATIONS
14-15 BERNERS STREET, LONDON, W1T 3LJ, UK.

EXCLUSIVE DISTRIBUTORS:
MUSIC SALES LIMITED
DISTRIBUTION CENTRE, NEWMARKET ROAD, BURY ST EDMUNDS,
SUFFOLK, IP33 3YB, UK.
MUSIC SALES PTY LIMITED
UNITS 3-4, 17 WILLFOX STREET, CONDELL PARK
NSW 2200, AUSTRALIA.

ORDER NO. AM1007171
ISBN 978-1-78305-235-6
THIS BOOK © COPYRIGHT 2013 BY WISE PUBLICATIONS,
A DIVISION OF MUSIC SALES LIMITED.

MUSIC ARRANGED BY FIONA BOLTON.
EDITED BY JENNI NOREY.
PRINTED IN THE EU.

TODAY'S HITS

Army Of Two

**Words & Music by Wayne Hector, Iyiola Babalola,
Darren Lewis & Olly Murs**

Olly Murs' 'Army Of Two' was written as a tribute to the X Factor success story's loyal fan base. To tie in with its release in February 2013, Murs launched a special Facebook application allowing his supporters to become members of the 'Olly Murs Army', by submitting their details and gaining a special membership ID and certificate. These unique IDs were later used in a fan video of the song uploaded to Murs' official YouTube channel.

Hints & Tips: Look out for E flat and B flat accidentals throughout. In bars 6–8, cross the second finger over the thumb to play the B flat.

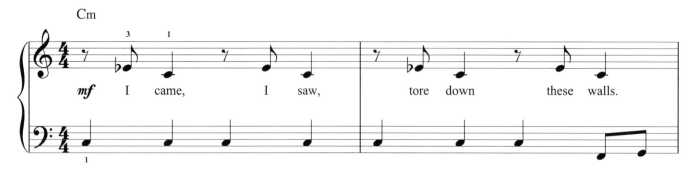

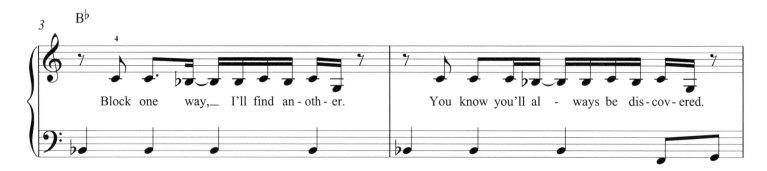

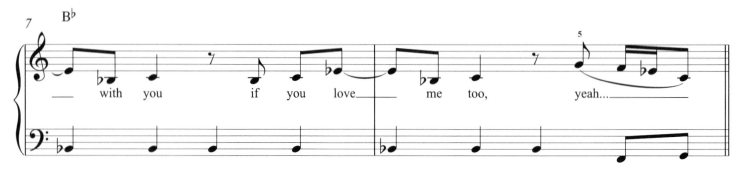

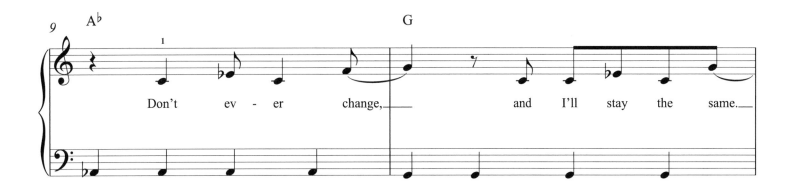

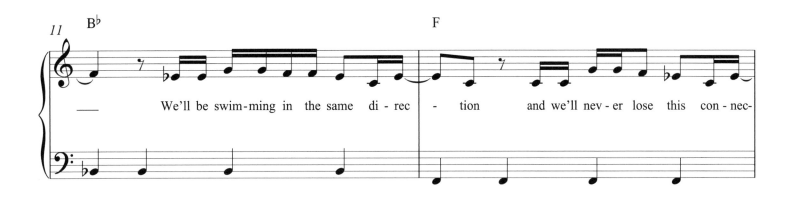

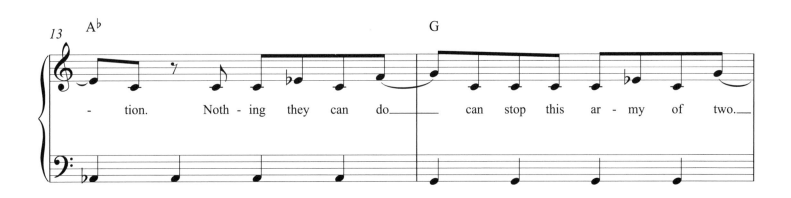

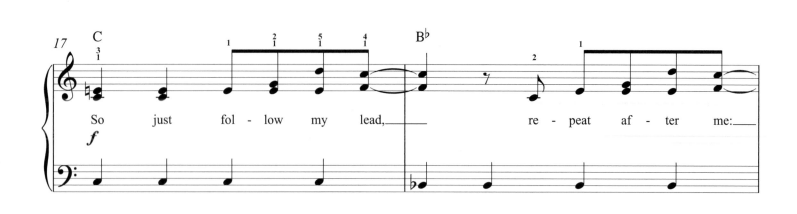

So just fol - low my lead,_____ re - peat af - ter me:___

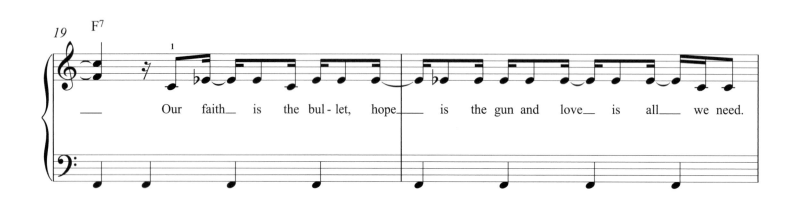

___ Our faith_ is the bul - let, hope_ is the gun and love_ is all_ we need.

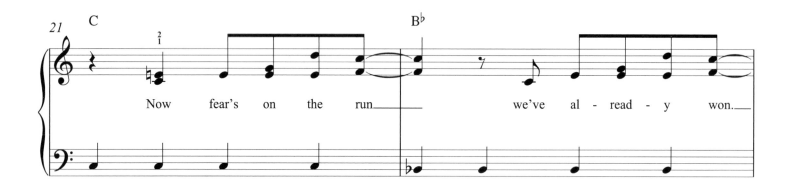

Now fear's on the run___ we've al - read - y won._

___ Now march_ with the band, raise_ your right hand. We've on - ly just_ be - gun.

Clown

Words & Music by Shahid Khan, Emeli Sandé & Grant Mitchell

BRIT Award winner Emeli Sandé's 2013 single 'Clown' talks about her experiences trying to forge a path through the music industry in the years before the release of her best-selling debut album, *Our Version Of Events*. Inspired by meetings with executives and agents who tried to pigeonhole Sandé and her music, the song's message is one of personal integrity and not allowing yourself or your work to be misjudged by others.

Hints & Tips: Although this is quite a slow song, some of the rhythms are quite fast. Be careful not to speed up so you have time to fit those semiquavers in.

8

Candy

Words & Music by Robbie Williams, Gary Barlow & Terje Olsen

'Candy' was released in 2012 as the lead single to Robbie Williams' ninth studio album, *Take The Crown*. An upbeat pop track, the song received positive reviews with many critics citing it as having a similar vibe to his previous smash hit 'Rock DJ'. The single topped the charts in the UK and achieved global success with top-ten positions in Austria, Germany, Ireland and the Netherlands.

Hints & Tips: From bar 17 the right hand is mostly playing thirds; make sure they sound nice and even.

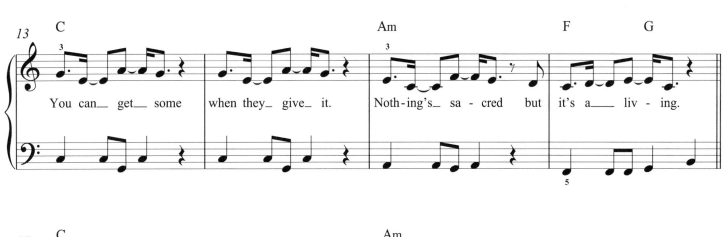

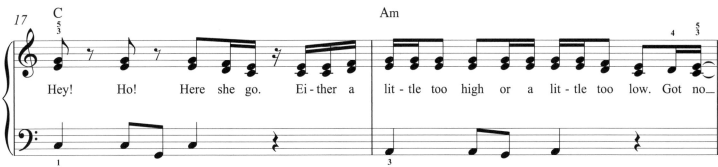

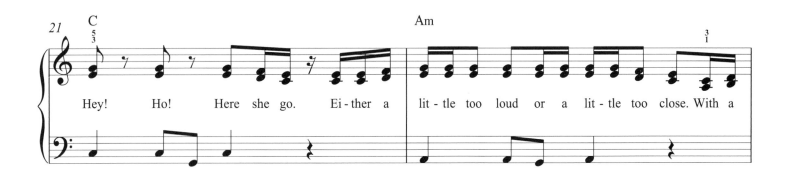

Change Your Life

**Words & Music by Richard Stannard, Ash Howes, Timothy Powell,
Jade Thirlwall, Perrie Edwards, Leigh-Anne Pinnock & Jesy Nelson**

'Change Your Life' was the first song directly written by Little Mix to be selected for release as a single from their debut album *DNA*. The song's themes are inspired by the band's whirlwind X Factor success and the positivity that helped them realise their dreams. The track is an uplifting number, reflecting the enthusiastic support the group received from their fans during their rise through the TV competition.

Hints & Tips: Practise the opening very slowly at first, paying attention to the changes in the right hand pattern, before building up to full speed.

Everything At Once

Words & Music by Lenka

Australian pop singer Lenka released 'Everything At Once' in 2012 as the third single from her album *Two*. While not a major success at first, the song and album rocketed up the charts after being featured in an advert for Microsoft's Windows 8 operating system.

Hints & Tips: The left hand is constantly leaping about in this. Play it through on its own until you are confident where your fingers will land!

Ho Hey

Words & Music by Jeremy Fraites & Wesley Schultz

Indie-folk band The Lumineers enjoyed a major breakthrough with 'Ho Hey' in 2012, reaching No. 1 in the USA and achieving Platinum certification. The song's success was helped along by being featured on a television spot for Microsoft's Bing search engine in June 2012, and it was later covered by Taylor Swift in a medley along with her own song 'Stay Stay Stay'.

Hints & Tips: The melody line, played by the right hand, shifts up an octave in bar 8. The two bars before are left hand only, so there's plenty of time to prepare.

How We Do (Party)

Words & Music by Hal David, Willie Hutch, Bob West, Jermaine Jackson, Bonnie McKee, Christopher Wallace, Andrew Harr, Alexander Delicata, Berry Gordy Jr., Osten Harvey, Kelly Sheehan, Andre Davidson & Sean Davidson

A punchy mix of pop, rock and dance, this song was the track that lifted UK singer-songwriter Rita Ora to global attention. Borrowing from the lyrics of hip-hip icon Notorious B.I.G., the track piqued the interest of Jay-Z and his Roc Nation label who promoted Ora and the single in the US leading to a placing on the Billboard 100.

Hints & Tips: Notice that the left hand is just one phrase repeated over and over. Keep the movement going by making sure you release each note; don't be tempted to hold them down for longer than the crotchet count.

Hurt Lovers

Words & Music by Jez Ashurst, David Jost, Martin Fliegenschmidt,
Alexander Zuckowski, Ryan Lee & James Duncan

Selected as the lead single for Blue's comeback album *Roulette*, 'Hurt Lovers' was the band's first official single release in two years following their Eurovision 2011 entry 'I Can'. Following its on-stage premiere during performances in China and Germany, the track became the official theme to the German romantic comedy film *Schlussmacher*.

Hints & Tips: Even though the notes played by the left hand change, note that the rhythm is the same in every bar.

If You Could See Me Now

Words & Music by Andrew Frampton, Stephen Kipner,
Mark Sheehan & Daniel O'Donoghue

This song is the emotionally charged 2013 single by The Script, written in tribute to the father of Danny O'Donoghue and the parents of guitarist Mark Sheehan, who died within months of each other when he was twelve years old. Lyrically, the song covers O'Donoghue and Sheehan's hopes that their loved ones are aware and proud of their musical achievements and lives as grown men.

Hints & Tips: In bars 6 and 10 the fifth and third fingers of the right hand need to cross over first and third. Practise this change over carefully until you can play it smoothly, as it crops up again later in the song.

Imagine It Was Us

Words & Music by Jessica Ware, David Corney,
Breyner Baptista, Julio Bashmore & James Napier

As a vocalist, Jessie Ware worked with the likes of Joder, Jack Peñate and SBTRKT both in the studio and in concert before achieving success with her own music. 'Imagine It Was Us' was the sixth single released from her debut album *Devotion*, which reached number five in the UK album charts upon its release in 2012.

Hints & Tips: Count the value of the rests as carefully as you would the notes, as they are just as important to the overall sound of the piece.

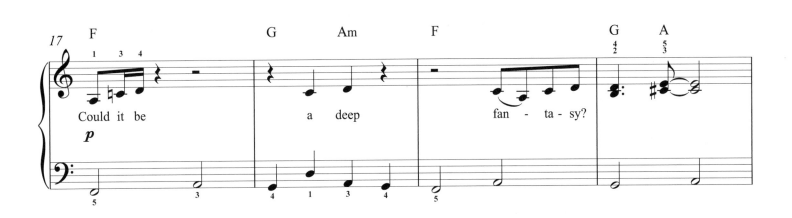

Impossible

Words & Music by Arnthor Birgisson & Ina Wroldsen

Released as his debut single after winning X Factor 2012, James Arthur's 'Impossible' rocketed to No. 1 in its first week of release, and has since gone on to sell over 1.3 million copies. Such impressive sales figures made it the best-selling single by an X Factor winner of all time, and with 490,000 units sold in its first week, the fastest selling single of the year in the UK.

Hints & Tips: The left hand plays only semibreves throughout, so really make the tune in the right hand come through.

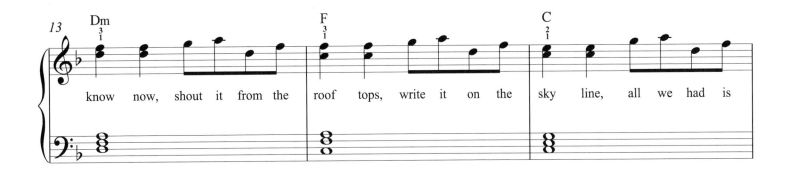

know now, shout it from the roof tops, write it on the sky line, all we had is

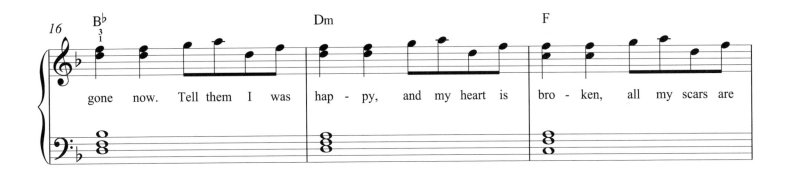

gone now. Tell them I was hap - py, and my heart is bro - ken, all my scars are

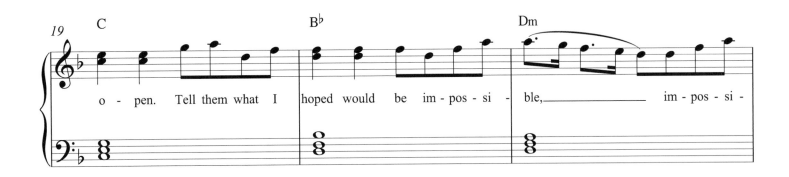

o - pen. Tell them what I hoped would be im - pos - si - ble, im - pos - si -

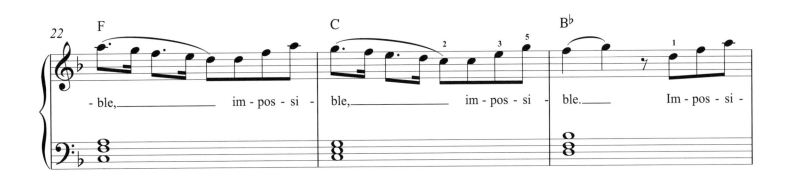

- ble, im - pos - si - ble, im - pos - si - ble. Im - pos - si -

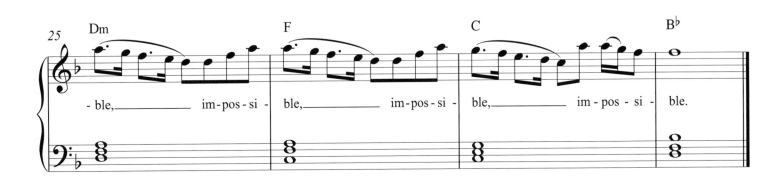

- ble, im - pos - si - ble, im - pos - si - ble, im - pos - si - ble.

Just Give Me A Reason

Words & Music by Alecia Moore, Jeff Bhasker
& Nate Ruess

'Just Give Me A Reason' is a duet featuring Nate Ruess, lead singer of Fun, and was the third single from P!nk's sixth studio album *The Truth About Love*. Even before its official release the song charted in multiple regions due to strong download sales. In the USA alone, the song eventually sold two million copies through digital downloads.

Hints & Tips: At the end of bar 28 you'll notice what looks like a comma. This means you should take a slight pause; try taking a deep breath before you begin bar 29.

Little Talks

Words & Music by Ragnar Thorhallsson & Nanna Bryndis Hilmarsdottir

Icelandic indie-folk-pop band Of Monsters And Men scored a Platinum-certified hit in 2012 with this breakthrough single. The lead single to their debut album, *My Head is an Animal*, the track catapulted the band to prominence in the USA thanks to national radio plays, with sales totalling two million copies as of March 2013.

Hints & Tips: There are a few performance directions in this, so make the most of them, particularly the *crescendo* in bar 16 and the *rit.* at the end.

truth may va-ry, this | ship will car-ry our | bod-ies safe to the shore. | Hey! Don't

lis-ten to a word I___ say. | Hey! The | screams all sound the___ same. | Hey! Al-though the

truth may va-ry, this | ship will car-ry our | bod-ies safe to the shore.

Hey! | Hey!

rit.

One Way Or Another (Teenage Kicks)

Words & Music by John O'Neill, Deborah Harry
& Nigel Harrison

A medley of Blondie's 'One Way Or Another' and 'Teenage Kicks' by the Undertones, One Direction's
'One Way Or Another (Teenage Kicks)' was released as the official single of Red Nose Day 2013. The song sold
113,000 copies in its first week, helping to raise funds for the Red Nose Day cause.

Hints & Tips: There are accidentals throughout, plus a key change and some chromatic passages- so watch out!

Picking Up The Pieces

Words & Music by Wayne Hector, Timothy Powell
& Paloma Faith

'Picking Up The Pieces' was inspired by Paloma Faith's experiences of insecurity while dating someone recovering from a previous relationship. The song's video is heavily influenced by David Lynch and his TV and film series *Twin Peaks* with the events on-screen taking a surreal twist as Faith turns into a melting waxwork, symbolising that her character was a figment of her imagination that never truly existed.

Hints & Tips: The right hand rhythms are often tied over to the next bar in this. Use the steady crotchets in the left hand to help you keep time.

_I was__ a bit_ more like__ her?____ Am I__ too__ loud?_

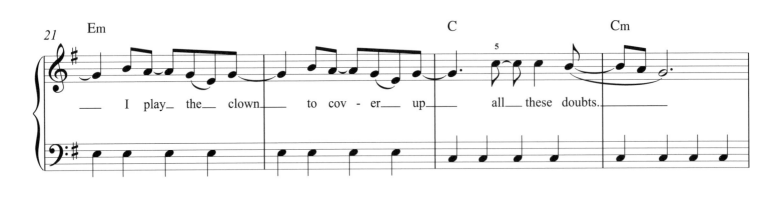

__ I play_ the__ clown___ to cov - er__ up___ all__ these doubts.____

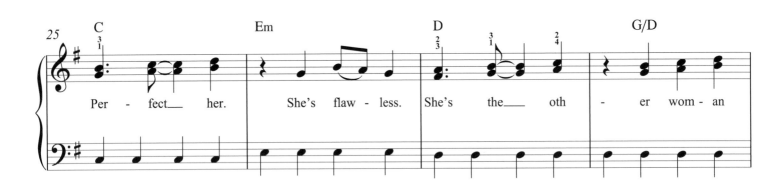

Per - fect__ her. She's flaw - less. She's the___ oth - er wom - an

shin - ing___ in her splen - dour. You were__ lost._____ Now she's

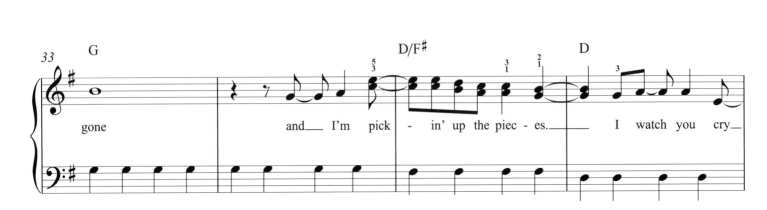

gone and__ I'm pick - in' up the piec - es.___ I watch you cry__

Please Don't Say You Love Me

Words & Music by Nicholas Atkinson & Gabrielle Aplin

Having risen to the attentions of the music world through the popular success of her acoustic covers of Paramore, Ben Howard and You Me At Six on YouTube, Gabrielle Aplin released her debut album *English Rain* in 2013. 'Please Don't Say You Love Me' was the second single released from the album and reached number six in the UK singles chart.

Hints & Tips: This is a fairly simple piece but it's quite fast. Keep things nice and steady and be careful not to rush too much.

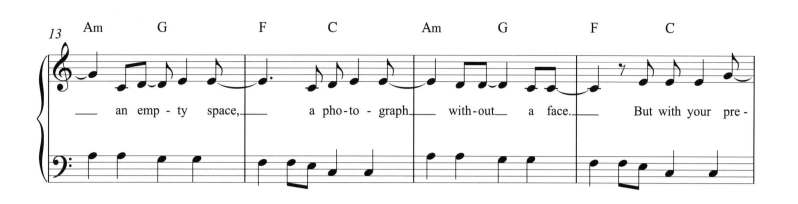

an emp - ty space,___ a pho-to-graph___ with-out___ a face.___ But with your pre-

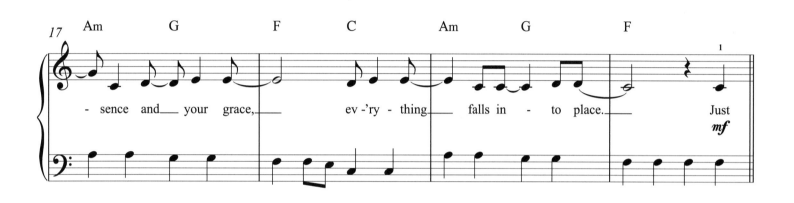

- sence and___ your grace,___ ev -'ry - thing___ falls in - to place.___ Just

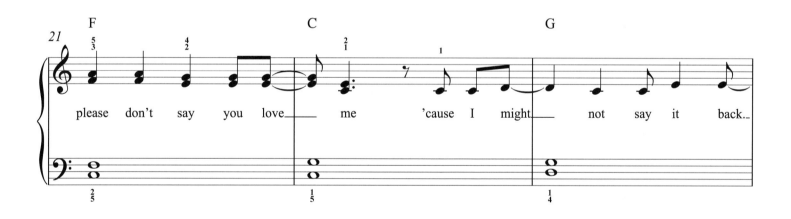

please don't say you love___ me 'cause I might___ not say it back.__

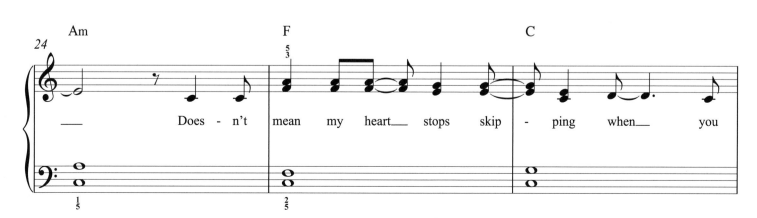

___ Does - n't mean my heart___ stops skip - ping when___ you

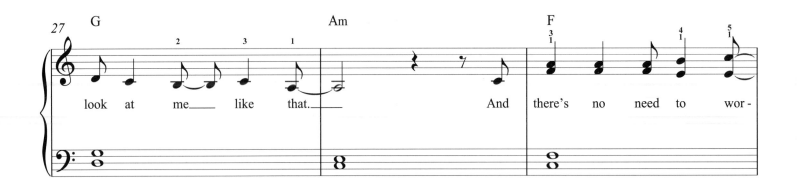

look at me___ like that.___ And there's no need to wor-

-ry when___ you see just where___ we're at.___ Just

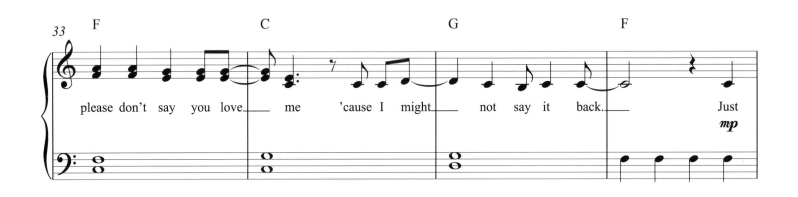

please don't say you love___ me 'cause I might___ not say it back.___ Just

please don't say you love___ me 'cause I might___ not say it back.___

Pompeii

Words & Music by Daniel Campbell Smith

Released as a digital download in February 2013, Bastille's 'Pompeii' peaked at No. 1 in the Irish singles chart for two consecutive weeks and number two in the UK. In Italy it was certified Platinum by the Federation of the Italian Music Industry and broke the record for the longest time spent at top of the UK's Official Streaming Chart.

Hints & Tips: Be careful not to start this one off to fast, otherwise the quavers on last page will become very tricky to play! Make sure left hand is smooth wherever it's playing two notes together.

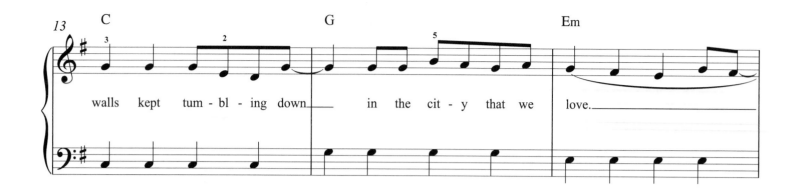

walls kept tum - bl - ing down____ in the cit - y that we love._____

____ Great clouds roll o - ver the hills____ bring - ing dark - ness from a -

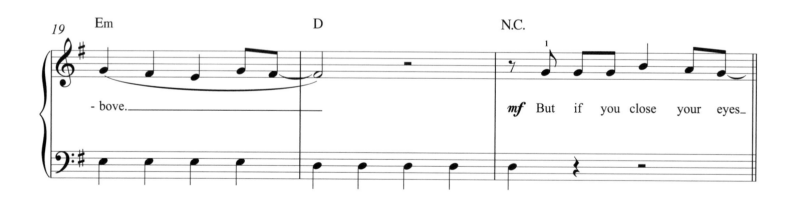

- bove._____ *mf* But if you close your eyes____

____ does it al - most feel____ like noth - ing changed at all?____

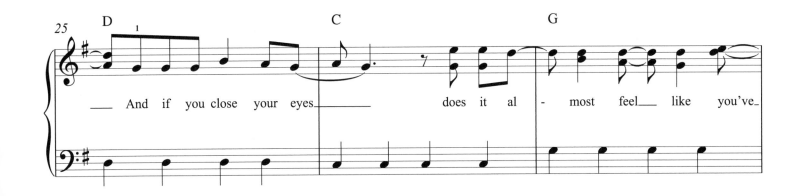

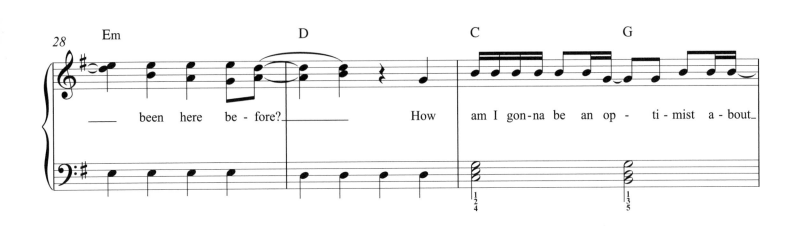

What About Us

Words & Music by Oliver Jacobs, Phillip Jacobs,
Sean Henriques & Camille Purcell

After debuting at No. 1 in the UK, 'What About Us' was selected to be The Saturdays' first international single, and the lead single to their first US-only EP *Chasing The Saturdays*. Two separate version of the song exist, one released in the UK and Ireland featuring Jamaican rapper Sean Paul, and a second version made exclusively for the US and Canada without any guest vocals.

Hints & Tips: The dotted quaver rhythmic pattern in the first half of bar 1 is one that is repeated all the way through. Count this out carefully before you begin.

23456789